A book
is a present you can open
again and again.

THIS BOOK BELONGS TO

_____

FROM

_____

Anytime Rhymes

CHIME-IN RHYMES

Illustrated by Linda Liefer

World Book, Inc.
a Scott Fetzer company
Chicago London Sydney Toronto

Copyright © 1992
World Book, Inc.
525 West Monroe Street
Chicago, Illinois 60661

Printed in the United States of America
ISBN 0-7166-1616-5
Library of Congress Catalog Card No. 91-65753

5 6 7 8 9 10 11 12 13 14 15 99 98 97 96 95 94

Cover design by Rosa Cabrera
Book design by Valerie Nelson-Metlay

What shall we do with a lazy Katie?
What shall we do with a lazy Katie?
What shall we do with a lazy Katie?
Early in the morning.

Roll her on the bed and tickle her all over,
Roll her on the bed and tickle her all over,
Roll her on the bed and tickle her all over,
Early in the morning.

Heave ho and UP she rises,
Heave ho and UP she rises,
Heave ho and UP she rises,
Early in the morning.

This is the way the ladies ride,
  Trit, trot, trit, trot.
This is the way the gentlemen ride,
  Jiggety-jog, jiggety-jog.
This is the way the farmers ride,
  Hobblety-hoy, hobblety-hoy.
This is the way the hunters ride,
  Gallopy, gallopy, gallopy,
    Over the fence.

Trot, trot to Boston,
Trot, trot to Lynn.
Look out baby—
You're going to fall in!

Father and Mother and Uncle John
Went to market, one by one.

Father fell off!

Mother fell off!

But Uncle John went on, and on,
And on, and on, and on.

Hob, shoe, hob,
Hob, shoe, hob.
    Here a nail,
    There a nail,
And that's well shod.

Shoe the horse,
With a tap-tap here.
Shoe the mare,
With a tap-tap there;
But let the little coltie
Go bare, bare, bare!

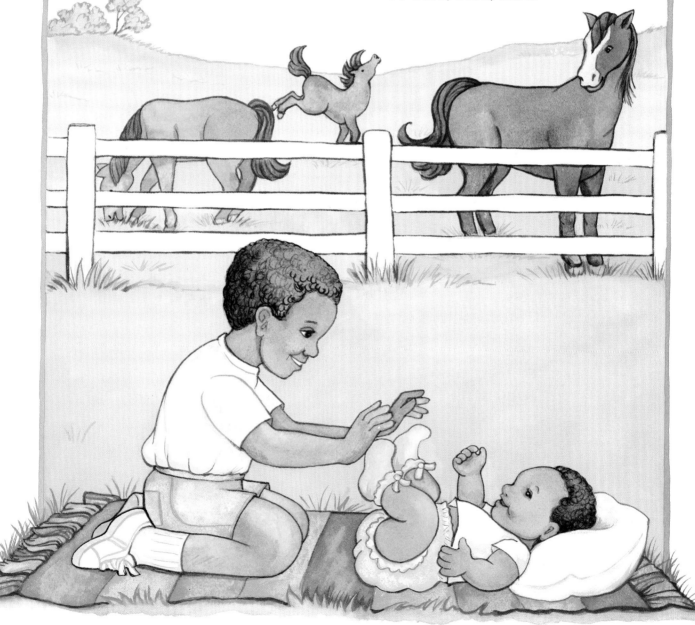

Leg over leg,
As the dog goes to Dover,
When he comes to a wall,
Jump!
He goes over!

Jack-in-the-box jumps UP like this.
He makes me laugh when he waggles his head.
I gently press him down again.
But Jack-in-the-box jumps up instead.

Pat-a-cake,
Pat-a-cake,
Baker's man,
Bake me a cake
As fast as you can.
Roll it,
And pat it,
And mark it with a "B,"
And put it in the oven
For baby and me!

Jeremiah, blow the fire,
Puff, puff, puff.
First you blow it gently,
Then you blow it rough.
Jeremiah, blow the fire,
PUFF, PUFF, PUFF!

Jelly on the plate,
Jelly on the plate,
Wibble, wobble,
Wibble, wobble,
Jelly on the plate.

Biscuits in the tin,
Biscuits in the tin,
Shake them up,
Shake them up,
Biscuits in the tin.

Fire on the floor,
Fire on the floor,
Stamp it out,
Stamp it out,
Fire on the floor.

Candles on the cake,
Candles on the cake,
Blow them out,
Blow them out,
Puff, puff, puff.

Down by the station,
Early in the morning,
See the little pufferbellies
All in a row.

See the stationmaster
Pull the little handle.

Chug! Chug!
Whoo! Whoo!
Off we go.

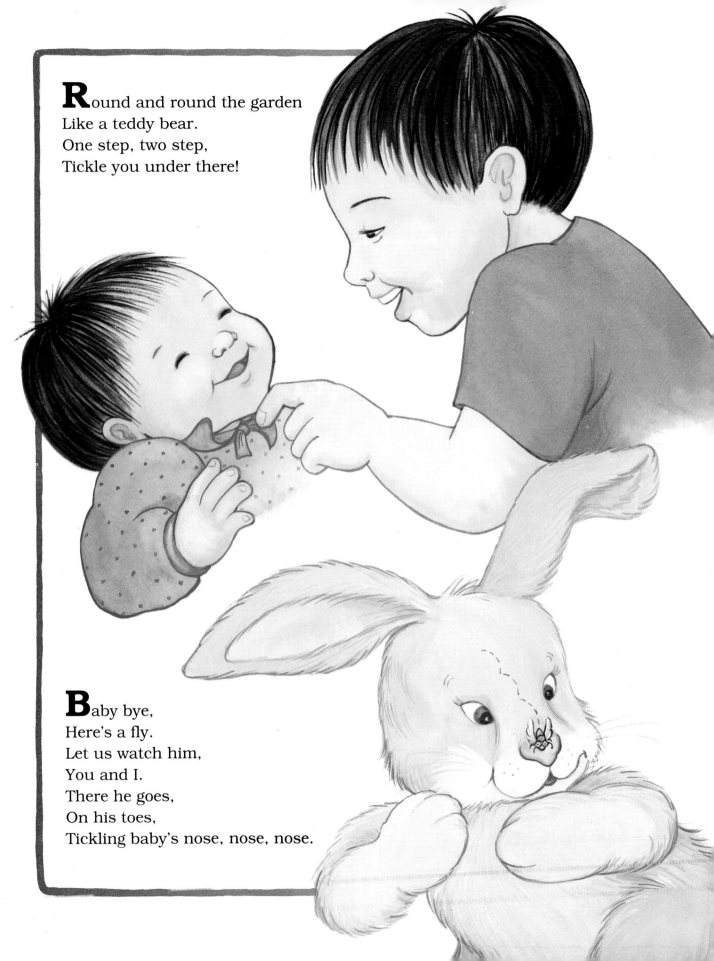

Round and round the garden
Like a teddy bear.
One step, two step,
Tickle you under there!

Baby bye,
Here's a fly.
Let us watch him,
You and I.
There he goes,
On his toes,
Tickling baby's nose, nose, nose.

Knock on the door,
  Peek in.
Lift up the latch,
  And walk in.

Head, shoulders, knees and toes, knees and toes,
Head, shoulders, knees and toes, knees and toes,
Eyes and ears and mouth and nose,
Head, shoulders, knees and toes, knees and toes!

Two little eyes
To look around.
Two little ears
To hear each sound.
One little nose
To smell what's sweet.
One little mouth
That likes to eat.

I have ten little fingers
And they all belong to me.
I can make them do things,
Would you like to see?
I can shut them up tight,
I can open them wide,
I can put them together,
And I can make them hide.
I can make them jump high,
I can make them jump low,
I can rolly them around
And fold them just so.

Johnny, Johnny, Johnny, Johnny,
Whoops, Johnny!
Whoops, Johnny!
Johnny, Johnny, Johnny, Johnny,
WHOOPS!

Wee Wiggie,
Poke Piggie,
Tom Whistle,
John Gristle,
And old BIG GOBBLE,
  Gobble, gobble!

This little piggy went to market;
This little piggy stayed home;
This little piggy ate roast beef;
This little piggy had none;
And this little piggy cried,
Wee-wee-wee-wee-wee,
All the way home.

Here goes a turtle up the hill—
  Creepy, creepy, creepy, creepy.
Here goes a rabbit up the hill—
  Boing, boing, boing, boing.
Here goes an elephant up the hill—
  Thud, thud, thud, thud.
Here goes a snake up the hill—
  Slither, slither, slither, slither.
Here comes a rock down the hill—
  Boom, boom, boom, boom, CRASH!

Two little blackbirds
Sitting on a hill;
One named Jack,
The other named Jill.

Fly away Jack!
Fly away Jill!

Come back Jack!
Come back Jill!

To market, to market,
To buy a fat pig;
Home again, home again,
Jiggety-jig.

To market, to market,
To buy a fat hog;
Home again, home again,
Jiggety-jog.

To market, to market,
To buy a plum bun;
Home again, home again,
Market is done.

Hickory, dickory, dock,
The mouse ran up the clock.
The clock struck one.
The mouse ran down,
Hickory, dickory, dock.

I can tie my shoelaces,
I can brush my hair,
I can wash my face and hands
And dry myself with care.

I can clean my teeth, too,
And fasten up my frocks.
I can dress all by myself
And pull up both my socks.

I'm a little teapot,
Short and stout.
Here is my handle;
Here is my spout.
When I get all steamed up,
Hear me shout:
"Just tip me over,
Pour me out!"

Can you walk on tiptoe as softly as a cat?
Can you stamp along the road STAMP, STAMP, just like that?
Can you take some great big strides just like a giant can?
Or walk along so slowly, like a bent old man?

Sally go round the sun,
Sally go round the moon,
Sally go round the chimney tops
Every afternoon.

London Bridge is falling down,
Falling down,
Falling down,
London Bridge is falling down,
My fair lady.

Ring-around o'rosies,
A pocket full of posies,
  A-tishoo! A-tishoo!
We all fall down.

The cows are in the meadow,
Lying fast asleep,
  A-tishoo! A-tishoo!
We all get up again.

If you're happy and you know it, clap your hands.
If you're happy and you know it, clap your hands.
If you're happy and you know it
Then your face will surely show it.
If you're happy and you know it, clap your hands.

If you're happy and you know it, stamp your feet.
If you're happy and you know it, stamp your feet.
If you're happy and you know it
Then your face will surely show it.
If you're happy and you know it, stamp your feet.

If you're happy and you know it, nod your head.
If you're happy and you know it, nod your head.
If you're happy and you know it
Then your face will surely show it.
If you're happy and you know it, nod your head.

If you're happy and you know it, shout "Hooray!"
If you're happy and you know it, shout "Hooray!"
If you're happy and you know it
Then your face will surely show it.
If you're happy and you know it, shout "HOORAY!"

Dance, little Baby, dance up high!
Never mind, Baby, Mother is by.
Crow and caper, caper and crow,
There, little Baby, there you go!
Up to the ceiling, down to the ground,
Backwards and forwards, round and round;
Dance, little Baby, and Mother will sing,
With the merry chorale, ding, ding, ding!

Dance to your daddy,
  My little baby,
Dance to your daddy,
  My little lamb.

You shall have a fishy
  In your little dishy,
You shall have a fishy
  When the boat comes in.

You shall have an apple,
  You shall have a plum,
You shall have a rattle-basket
  When your daddy comes home.

Stepping over stepping stones,
One, two, three.
Stepping over stepping stones,
Come with me.
The river's very fast,
And the river's very wide.
And we'll step across the stepping stones
And reach the other side.

Row, row, row your boat
Gently down the stream.
Merrily, merrily, merrily, merrily,
Life is but a dream.

Wee Willie Winkie runs through the town,
Upstairs and downstairs in his nightgown,
Rapping on the window, crying through the lock,
"Are the children all in bed, for now it's eight o'clock?"

Diddle, diddle, dumpling,
    my son John,
Went to bed with his
    trousers on;
One shoe off, and
    one shoe on,
Diddle, diddle, dumpling,
    my son John.

Hush-a-bye,
  don't you cry,
Go to sleepy,
  little baby.

When you wake, you
  shall have a cake
And all the pretty
  little horses.

Blacks and bays,
  and dapples and grays,
Coach and six
  white horses.

The Man in the Moon looked
    out of the moon,
Looked out of the moon
    and said:
"'Tis time for all children
    on the earth
To think about going to bed!"

To Parents

Infants and children love to share rhymes, chants, and songs with their parents. *Chime-In Rhymes* is filled with these types of verses. They will provide hours of entertainment, as well as a bridge for your child into developing some important skills. Here are just a few easy and natural ways your child can express feelings and understandings about the verses. You know your child and can best judge which ideas she or he will enjoy most.

You and your child can tape-record your favorite verses from the book. The tape will have many entertaining uses. For example, you can play the tape while reading the verses at home, driving in the car, and doing chores. And you can listen to the tape anytime you are moving, dancing, or playing together.

To make up your own motions to verses, ask your child questions such as, "How do you blow out the candles?" or "How does the turtle go up the hill?" Encourage your child to act out each verse.

You and your child may enjoy adding sound effects to these verses. Help your child select objects in the pictures and imitate the sounds the objects make. Include the sounds when you say the verses.

Play with the verses by asking your child to suggest new lines. Use your child's responses in the verses. For example, ask your child questions such as, "What else can you do with a Lazy Katie?" "Who else went to market?" "What else wiggles on a plate?"

Here's another way to create verses with your child. Find book, catalog, or magazine pictures of children who are doing things that you and your child enjoy. Make up your own verses, or recite verses from the book to tell about the pictures.

Any activity you do with your child provides an opportunity to enjoy making up your own rhymes, chants, and songs. These can be about what you are doing at the moment, other things you do during the day, or people you know.